Garfield Strikes Again

JIM DAVIS

RAVETTE BOOKS

First published by Ravette Books Limited 1984
Reprinted 1985, 1986, 1987
This edition first published 1988
Reprinted 1988, 1989, 1990

Printed and bound in Great Britain
for Ravette Books Limited,
3 Glenside Estate, Star Road, Partridge Green,
Horsham, West Sussex RH13 8RA
by Cox & Wyman Ltd, Reading

ISBN 0 906710 62 6

OKAY, WHO LOOSENED THE TOP ON MY SALTSHAKER?!
JIM DAVIS

GARFIELD, THAT WASN'T VERY NICE
YOU'RE RIGHT. THAT WASN'T VERY NICE

BUT IT WAS EXTREMELY FUNNY
1-5-84

WHO'S THAT PANTING AT MY DOOR?
JIM DAVIS 3-5

HONK HONK

OH, GOOD MORNING, ODIE
HONK

YAWN
3-6
JIM DAVIS

GASP!

WAKING UP TO MY OWN BAD BREATH IS BAD ENOUGH, BUT SOMEONE ELSE'S IS UNBEARABLE

I AM PROUD TO BE A PET. PETS LEND A TOUCH OF ELEGANCE TO A HOME
SLUP SLUP
JIM DAVIS
© 1984 United Feature Syndicate,Inc.

I AM PROUD TO BE A CAT
SLUP SLUP
3-7

OKAY, GET REVVED UP THERE, ODIE
3-8
JIM DAVIS

GO!

I LOVE TOYS THAT DON'T NEED BATTERIES

JIM DAVIS
3-9

CRINKLE

MAY I HAVE SOME OF THAT CANDY BAR?
HERE, TAKE IT
ICH

3-10

I DECLARE THIS STEAK THE SOVEREIGN PROPERTY OF GARFIELD, THE CAT!
JIM DAVIS

I'VE NEVER HAD MY DINNER ANNEXED BEFORE
AND YOU MAY NEVER SEE IT ALIVE AGAIN
© 1984 United Feature Syndicate,Inc.

GIMME THOSE COOKIES
3-27
JIM DAVIS

HIYA! HUT!
KONK!
PUNT!

I'D TURN HER IN, BUT WHO'D ADMIT TO BEING MANGLED BY A GIRL SCOUT?

I WONDER HOW FAST I CAN RUN
JIM DAVIS
1-30

I WONDER WHAT WOULD HAPPEN IF I HIT THIS KITTY DOOR AT MACH 2

I WONDER IF KILLING A MAILMAN IS A FEDERAL OFFENSE

I LOVE ATTACKING THE MAILMAN. SOME DAYS I SCRATCH HIM. SOME DAYS I BITE HIM. SOME DAYS I TRIP HIM

TODAY I'M TRYING SOMETHING NEW
♪

I'M HUMILIATING HIM
JIM DAVIS
1-31

JIM DAVIS 2-1

ARRRGH!
B-B-B-B

WHEN HE COMES AROUND, HE'LL THANK ME FOR BREAKING UP THE MONOTONY OF HIS DREARY JOB
© 1984 United Feature Syndicate, Inc.

COME ON, MAILMAN, DELIVER THAT MAIL
JIM DAVIS
2-2

AND WHEN YOU DO, I'M GOING TO LEAP ON YOU AND ALL THAT WILL BE LEFT WILL BE YOUR MAILBAG AND THAT SILLY-LOOKING HAT OF YOURS

HAS THE MAILMAN COME YET, GARFIELD?
NO, HE'S STILL STANDING AT THE END OF THE SIDEWALK SOBBING
© 1984 United Feature Syndicate, Inc.

SLAM!
JIM DAVIS
2·3

RATS! I MISSED HIM

APPARENTLY, NO ONE EVER TOLD HIM TO LOOK BOTH WAYS BEFORE CROSSING THE STREET
SCREECH
© 1984 United Feature Syndicate, Inc.

I'LL CUT THE LASAGNA IN TWO PIECES, AND YOU TAKE FIRST PICK
JIM DAVIS
5-21

IT'S GETTING COLD, GARFIELD

YOU REALLY SHOULD THINK ABOUT JOGGING, GARFIELD. IT'S 50% MENTAL, YOU KNOW
IT IS?
JIM DAVIS
5-20

GREAT!

JOG, JOG, JOG. JOG, JOG, JOG. PANT, PANT. SWEAT
I'LL WORK ON THE OTHER 50% SOME OTHER TIME
© 1982 United Feature Syndicate, Inc.

BE A GOOD BOY AND FETCH THE MAIL, GARFIELD
OUI, MON CAPITAINE
2-4
JIM DAVIS

RIP
ROWR
CLOBBER
BLAP

DID YOU HURT HIM BAD?
OH, JUST A FEW LACERATIONS, ABRASIONS AND INTERNAL INJURIES. I WAS IN A GOOD MOOD

BRINNNG!
JIM DAVIS
1-3-83

WHAM!

BRINNNG!

GARFIELD, WHY IS IT CATS LIKE TO GET OUT AT NIGHT?
4-27
JIM DAVIS

THAT'S WHEN WE LIKE TO SING ON FENCES

IN THE DAYLIGHT, WE'D BE EASY TARGETS
© 1983 United Feature Syndicate, Inc.

LET US EXAMINE A PET PHENOMENON CALLED THE "RIPS"
JIM DAVIS
1-19

THAT'S WHEN YOUR PETS RACE AROUND THE HOUSE FOR NO APPARENT REASON

OTHER THAN TO MANGLE THE FAMILY CAT
© 1984 United Feature Syndicate,Inc.

YOU BOYS STOP RACING AROUND
JIM DAVIS
1·20

GARFIELD, SLOW DOWN!

OKAY

WOULD YOU LIKE TO GO FOR A WALK, ODIE ?
JIM DAVIS
1-21

LET'S SEE... I NEED A LEASH

YOU STAY OUT OF THIS
© 1984 United Feature Syndicate,Inc.

JIM DAVIS
12-9

MY NEWSPAPER! YOU CHEWED UP MY NEWSPAPER!

IT'S THINGS LIKE THIS THAT MAKE ME WONDER IF YOU SHOULD BRING IN THE PAPER AT ALL
PRECISELY
POO

I GOTTA BEAT THAT FLY TO MY FOOD!
JIM DAVIS
3-22

I WIN!

YOU LOSE, FELLA
POO
GARFIELD
© 1984 United Feature Syndicate, Inc.

JIM DAVIS

WHEW
3·23
© 1984 United Feature Syndicate, Inc.

BOO!

JIM DAVIS

REARRR!
3-24

IT'S THE OLD "BRING IN THE REINFORCEMENTS" TRICK

HERE YOU GO, GARFIELD. TAKE A BIG BITE
JIM DAVIS
11-21

OH NO!

JUST KIDDING

GARFIELD, I THINK YOU'RE TOO MEAN TO ODIE
JIM DAVIS 6-25

I NEVER WANT TO SEE YOU HIT HIM AGAIN
OH, VERY WELL

KONK!

I'M GOING TO THE STORE, GARFIELD. IF YOU LAY A PAW ON ODIE, I'LL SPANK YOU

BOING
JIM DAVIS
6-26

GARFIELD, I SWEAR YOU'VE DONE EVERYTHING TO ODIE A CAT COULD DO TO A DOG
AU CONTRAIRE
JIM DAVIS

PLINK

NEVER UNDERESTIMATE ME

HEY, ODIE! I FOUND YOUR NOSE!

LET ME PUT IT ON FOR YOU, PAL
SQUIK SQUIK

VERY NICE. I LIKE YOU AS A RAT TERRIER
SNIFF
JIM DAVIS
6·28

WELL, WELL, WELL. I SEE YOU'RE EATING MY FOOD, ODIE. NOW WHAT ARE WE GOING TO DO WITH YOU?
GARFIELD
JIM DAVIS
6-29

WE ARE GOING TO KICK YOU INTO NEXT WEEK! THAT'S WHAT WE'RE GOING TO DO!
PUNT
GARFIELD

WHERE'S ODIE?
SOMEWHERE OVER SATURDAY

LUNCH ISN'T THE SAME WITHOUT ODIE. HE ALWAYS SLIPS UP BEHIND ME, BARKS LOUDLY AND MAKES ME FALL INTO MY FOOD
GARFIELD
JIM DAVIS 6-30

I GUESS I'LL JUST HAVE TO MAKE DO
GARFIELD

BLUT
GARFIELD

I'M WORKING UP A ROUTINE FOR THE FENCE TONIGHT, POOKY. TELL ME WHAT YOU THINK OF IT
JIM DAVIS
7-4

I KNEW A TEDDY BEAR WHO WAS SO UGLY, EVEN THE TIDE WOULDN'T TAKE IT OUT

BLAT!

GOOD EVENING, LADIES AND GERMS. I'D LIKE YOU TO MEET POOKY, MY GAG WRITER
JIM DAVIS
7-5

SPLAT
© 1984 United Feature Syndicate, Inc.

WELCOME TO SHOW BIZ, KID

JUMP THROUGH THE HOOP, POOKY
JIM DAVIS

HEY, GARFIELD. WHAT'S HAPPENING?
I'M PRETENDING TO TEACH POOKY TRICKS

© 1984 United Feature Syndicate, Inc.
7-6

BUTTERFLIES ARE VERSATILE. THEY CAN CARESS THE AIR
JIM DAVIS 7-7

THEY CAN KISS THE DEW FROM THE FLOWERS

AND THEY CAN EMBED THEMSELVES IN RADIATORS
FWAP!

I HAVE THIS NAGGING FEELING I'M FORGETTING SOMETHING
JIM DAVIS
7-2

WHUMP!

OH YES, I FORGOT I KICKED ODIE INTO NEXT WEEK, LAST WEEK

Z
JIM DAVIS
2-21

BARK!

I SEE YOU'RE BRINGING THE MAIL IN WITH YOUR USUAL CARE
JIM DAVIS
12-8

THIS LETTER SAYS, "DO NOT FOLD, SPINDLE OR MUTILATE"

IT DIDN'T SAY ANYTHING ABOUT "MAUL"

AWK!
JIM DAVIS
3-19

I LOVE CHASING BIRDS

EXCEPT WHEN THEY DO THAT

BONK!
RATS!
3-20
JIM DAVIS

DOUBLE RATS!

AND, OF COURSE, TRIPLE RATS

HEH HEH
RATTLE RATTLE
JIM DAVIS
12-26

CATS HAVE SUCH ACTIVE IMAGINATIONS. I WONDER WHAT'S GOING ON IN GARFIELD'S MIND RIGHT NOW

WELL... HERE I AM, IN A BROWN PAPER BAG
© 1983 United Feature Syndicate, Inc.

INTERESTING
12·27
JIM DAVIS

RESIDING IN A BROWN PAPER BAG GIVES ONE AN ALL-NEW PERSPECTIVE ON ONE'S SELF

I FEEL LIKE A DIRTY MAGAZINE

THIS BAG NEEDS EYEHOLES
12-28
JIM DAVIS

RUSTLE
RIP
RUSTLE

SOMETHING'S NOT RIGHT HERE

GOT MY SACK, GOT MY EYEHOLES, WHAT MORE COULD A CAT NEED?
JIM DAVIS
12-29

ARRRRGH!

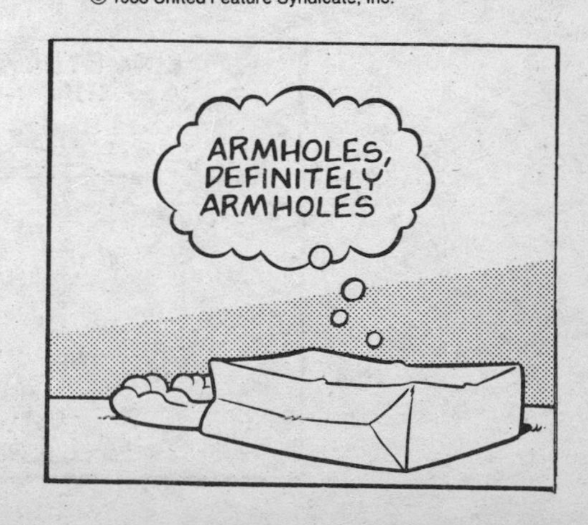
ARMHOLES, DEFINITELY ARMHOLES

AWK! THERE'S SOMEONE IN THIS BAG WITH ME
JIM DAVIS
12-30

OH, IT'S YOU

HELLO, BELLYBUTTON

FFFFF
JIM DAVIS
12-31

POW!

I DIDN'T KNOW YOU WERE IN THE BAG, GARFIELD. I WAS PLAYING A TRICK ON ODIE
AT LEAST I DIED FOR A GOOD CAUSE

I AM ABSOLUTELY NOT GETTING OUT OF BED TODAY
JIM DAVIS
5-9

HEY, GARFIELD, THERE'S A SPIDER ON YOUR BLANKET

I KEEP FORGETTING WE LIVE IN A GENERATION WITHOUT ABSOLUTES

I'LL TEACH HIM TO BE A SPIDER!
STOMP STOMP STOMP
STOMP STOMP
5-10

HE WON'T HAVE THE GUTS TO DO THAT AGAIN

 JIM DAVIS

BETTER SAFE THAN SORRY
STOMP STOMP
STOMP STOMP STOMP

LOOK AT THIS
JIM DAVIS
5-11

A CAT STROKING HIS OWNER!

WHY SO AFFECTIONATE, GARFIELD?
I JUST SQUASHED A SPIDER
© 1984 United Feature Syndicate,Inc.

GARFIELD
5-12
JIM DAVIS

SLUG

BIG DAY
GARFIELD

I HATE MONDAYS
GARFIELD, I DON'T KNOW WHY YOU HATE MONDAYS SO MUCH
5-28
JIM DAVIS

BLAT!

SEE?!!!

GOOD MORNING, GARFIELD
5-29
JIM DAVIS

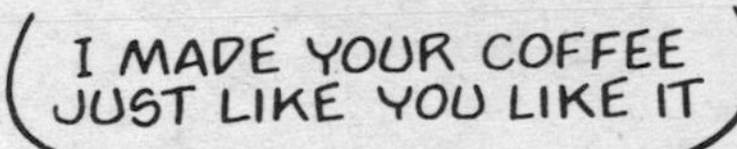
I MADE YOUR COFFEE JUST LIKE YOU LIKE IT

STRONG

OH SHUCKS, I JUST SPILLED THE ONLY CUP OF COFFEE WE HAVE IN THE HOUSE
JIM DAVIS
5-30

1-23
JIM DAVIS

GOOD MORNING, GARFIELD. IT'S ME, NERMAL. I'M YOUNG AND GOOD-LOOKING AND YOU'RE NOT

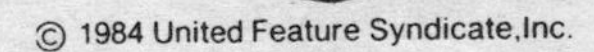

I DIDN'T NEED THAT

CAN I GET YOU ANYTHING FOR BREAKFAST, GARFIELD?
1-24
JIM DAVIS

YEAH, HOW ABOUT A BIG GLASS OF FRESHLY-SQUEEZED KITTEN JUICE?

YOU DON'T LIKE ME, DO YOU?
© 1984 United Feature Syndicate, Inc.

HOW CUTE! NERMAL BROUGHT ME MY NEWSPAPER
JIM DAVIS
1-25

AND MY SLIPPERS AND MY PIPE! WHAT MORE COULD A MAN WANT?

HOW ABOUT A WOMAN?

LET'S GET YOU INTO TROUBLE, NERMAL
COOKIES
1-26
JIM DAVIS

LOOK IN THE COOKIE JAR! LOOK IN THE COOKIE JAR!
NO, YOU CAN'T HAVE A COOKIE, GARFIELD. YOU'LL SPOIL DINNER
COOKIES

THANKS FOR THE COOKIES
JEFF WOULD HAVE KNOWN WHAT LASSIE WAS TALKING ABOUT
COOKIES

ODIE
JIM DAVIS
1-27

BLUT, BLUT!

CALL IT CRUEL.
CALL IT JUVENILE.
I CALL IT ASSERTING
MYSELF
ODIE

I HATE TO BOTHER YOU, SIR, BUT YOU PUT INSUFFICIENT POSTAGE ON YOUR PACKAGE

WHAT PACKAGE?

THIS KITTEN YOU'RE SENDING TO ABU DHABI
GARFIELD
JIM DAVIS 1-28

HEY, GARFIELD, IT SAYS HERE PEOPLE CAN PERFORM SUPER-HUMAN FEATS OF STRENGTH DURING PERIODS OF GREAT STRESS
2-6

WHAT BALONEY!

BY THE WAY, I'M TAKING YOU TO THE VET TODAY
JIM DAVIS

YOU CAN'T HIDE FROM ME FOREVER, GARFIELD. I'M GOING TO FIND YOU AND TAKE YOU TO THE VET
JIM DAVIS

YOU MAY BE SNEAKY, BUT I'M SNEAKIER

"SNEAKY" IS MY MIDDLE NAME
2-7
© 1984 United Feature Syndicate, Inc.

GARFIELD CAN'T RESIST LASAGNA, AND WHEN HE COMES TO EAT IT, I'M GOING TO CATCH HIM AND TAKE HIM TO THE VET
JIM DAVIS
2-8

SMACK
GULP
SLURP

THAT CAT HAS THE LONGEST LIPS I'VE EVER SEEN

NOW WHERE COULD GARFIELD BE?
Biscuits
COOKIES
2-9
JIM DAVIS

HE'S NOT IN THE COOKIES, AND HE CERTAINLY WOULDN'T BE IN THE DOGGIE BISCUITS
Biscuits
COOKIES

IT'S A GOOD THING I CAN'T READ
POO!
Biscuits
COOKIES
© 1984 United Feature Syndicate, Inc.

AHA! THERE YOU ARE, GARFIELD! YOU'RE GOING TO THE VET NOW
JIM DAVIS

SORRY, ODIE
SMACK
2-10

I WISH I COULD FIND GARFIELD'S HIDING PLACE SO I COULD TAKE HIM TO THE VET
JIM DAVIS
2-11

HE'S SURE HIDING IN A GOOD PLACE

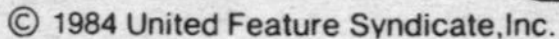

A GOOD PLACE-- NOT A SMART PLACE-- BUT A GOOD PLACE

IF PEOPLE HAD HAIR ALL OVER THEIR BODIES, WOULD THEY WEAR CLOTHING ?
JIM DAVIS

2-14

PROBABLY NOT

WHAT WOULD HAPPEN IF PEOPLE WERE CATS AND CATS WERE PEOPLE?

THAT'S AN EASY ONE

JIM DAVIS 2-15
DOGS WOULD SOON BECOME EXTINCT

I WAS WONDERING, GARFIELD...
© 1984 United Feature Syndicate, Inc.

WHAT IF BEING FAT WERE CONSIDERED ATTRACTIVE?

WHAT DO YOU MEAN, "WHAT IF," BOZO?
JIM DAVIS 2-16

THIS IS YOUR CONSCIENCE SPEAKING. DON'T YOU DARE PUSH ODIE OFF THE TABLE! THAT WOULD BE INHUMANE AND CRUEL
GARFIELD

THEN **YOU** PUSH HIM OFF
POKE!
GARFIELD
2-21

THAT WAS KIND OF FUN
© 1984 United Feature Syndicate, Inc.
JIM DAVIS

I WONDER WHAT LIFE WOULD BE LIKE IF WE NEVER HAD TO EAT

IT WOULD TAKE SOME GETTING USED TO

FOR A TIME, MOTHERS WOULD FIX THEIR FAMILIES THREE SQUARE NOTHINGS A DAY
JIM DAVIS 2·17

WHAT IF THERE WERE NEVER A LEONARDO DA VINCI?

THAT WOULD BE AWFUL!

THE DA VINCI KIDS WOULD HAVE BEEN ORPHANS
JIM DAVIS 2-18

I HATE MONDAYS
JIM DAVIS
2-20

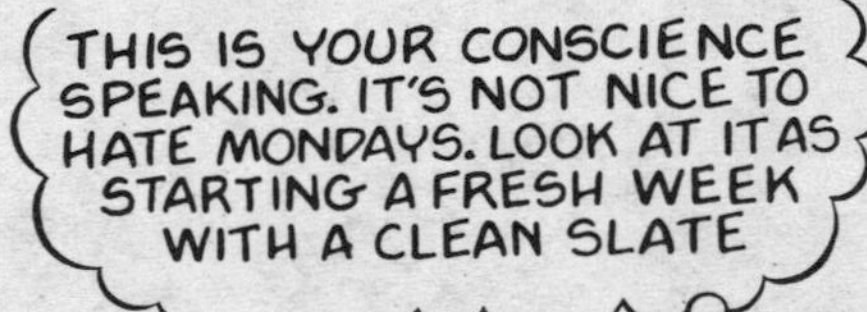
THIS IS YOUR CONSCIENCE SPEAKING. IT'S NOT NICE TO HATE MONDAYS. LOOK AT IT AS STARTING A FRESH WEEK WITH A CLEAN SLATE

I HATE MONDAYS
© 1984 United Feature Syndicate, Inc.

WHAT ODIE NEEDS IS A GOOD KICK

UH-OH! NAP ATTACK!

I DON'T EVEN WANT TO KNOW
Z
7-24
JIM DAVIS

WHY DO YOU FOLLOW ME AROUND, CONSCIENCE?
IF I DON'T, YOU WON'T BE VERY NICE

IF I PUT THIS CORK IN YOUR BOTTLE WOULD YOU BE TRAPPED?
YES, BUT THAT WOULDN'T BE VERY NICE

THAT WASN'T VERY NICE
© 1984 United Feature Syndicate, Inc.
JIM DAVIS
2-22

NOW THAT MY CONSCIENCE IS TRAPPED IN THIS BOTTLE, I CAN WALK AWAY AND ENJOY MYSELF
2·23

THAT'S OKAY, GO AHEAD, HAVE FUN, DON'T WORRY ABOUT ME. I'LL JUST SIT HERE IN THE DARK... ALL ALONE

 JIM DAVIS

YOU'RE VERY GOOD
ONE OF THE BEST

LET'S HAVE SOME FUN, GARFIELD. TAKE ONE STEP BACK
OKAY
JIM DAVIS
2-24

I THOUGHT CONSCIENCES WERE SUPPOSED TO BE NICE!
I'M ON BREAK

I HAVE MY CONSCIENCE TRAPPED IN THIS BOTTLE. I'LL JUST SET IT BY JON
JIM DAVIS
2-25

GET A HAIRCUT

EVERY MORNING FOR NEARLY SIX YEARS NOW, I FIX RAISIN TOAST FOR GARFIELD

JIM DAVIS 6-12
HE LOVES HIS RAISIN TOAST
© 1984 United Feature Syndicate, Inc.

WHAT'S IN THE DRAWER?
A SIX-YEAR SUPPLY OF RAISINS

ROWR
5-31

WHOCK!

GARFIELD, WHERE DID THE FLOWERS COME FROM?!
WELL, WHY DON'T WE JUST READ THE NOTE?
JIM DAVIS

YOU LIKE TO SCRATCH THINGS, DON'T YOU, GARFIELD?
DOES A CHICKEN LIKE TO PECK? SURE I DO!
JIM DAVIS
6-1

GOOD! SCRATCH MY BACK

NO CLAWS! NO CLAWS!
IF I DIDN'T USE CLAWS, I WOULDN'T BE SCRATCHING, NOW WOULD I?
© 1984 United Feature Syndicate, Inc.

SCRATCH HIGHER, GARFIELD
JIM DAVIS

HIGHER!
6-2

GET OFF THE CURTAINS, GARFIELD
I WAS JUST FOLLOWING INSTRUCTIONS
© 1984 United Feature Syndicate, Inc.

JIM DAVIS 8-15

RIIIP!

CRUELTY IS SECOND NATURE TO THAT CAT
© 1983 United Feature Syndicate, Inc.

BONK!
BONK!
JIM DAVIS

BONK!
BONK!
11-2

ODIE'S GOING TO HAVE TO LEARN TO WALK ONE OF THESE DAYS
© 1983 United Feature Syndicate, Inc.

I WANTED TO BUY YOU ANOTHER BED, GARFIELD. BUT THE ONLY SIZES THEY CAME IN WERE SMALL, MEDIUM AND LARGE
GARFIELD
10·5
JIM DAVIS

THEY DIDN'T HAVE SHOWBOAT!
GARFIELD

A QUICK WIT IS BEST ACCOMPANIED BY QUICK REFLEXES

JIM DAVIS 6-11

DON'T YOU DARE
I DON'T KNOW WHAT YOU'RE TALKING ABOUT

STOP BEGGING, GARFIELD.
YOU MAY HAVE ANY FOOD
THAT FALLS ON THE FLOOR

JIM DAVIS 4-13
I HATE YOU
I CAN LIVE WITH THAT

COOKIES
JIM DAVIS
6-30

COOKIES

COOKIE

JIM DAVIS 4·14
HEE-HEE, SNORT

WAH-HA-HA!

OKAY! OKAY! I'M AWAKE!

I LOVE IT WHEN THE GOOD HUMOR MAN COMES
DING DING
JIM DAVIS
1-16

I LOVE IT WHEN I GET A POPSICLE

I HATE IT WHEN MY LIPS STICK TO THE ☆◎⚡! POPSICLE

EVER NOTICE HOW MOTHS CIRCLE THE LIGHT?
JIM DAVIS
1-17

LIKE PLANETS ORBITING A DISTANT SUN

I LOVE IT WHEN I GET PHILOSOPHICAL
© 1984 United Feature Syndicate,Inc.

I WONDER WHAT HAPPENS WHEN A MOTH GETS TOO CLOSE TO THE LIGHT
JIM DAVIS
1-18

AYIEEEE!
FOOM!

AT LEAST HE DIDN'T SUFFER

RISE AND SHINE, GARFIELD. IT'S A BRIGHT NEW DAY!
1-2-84
JIM DAVIS

IT'S GONNA BE A WONDERFUL DAY, A GREAT DAY!

I THINK I OVER-CHEERFULED IT

HOW DO YOU WANT YOUR COFFEE, GARFIELD?
MAKE IT SIT UP AND BARK
JIM DAVIS 1-3-84

HOW'S THIS?

JUST RIGHT

SHOO!
GARFIELD
JIM DAVIS
3-21

FLIES AND I HAVE A LOT IN COMMON...
GARFIELD

YOU CAN'T KEEP EITHER OF US AWAY FROM FOOD
GARFIELD

JIM DAVIS
7-13

WAH-HA HA-HA!
I HATE IT WHEN THEY DO THAT
© 1983 United Feature Syndicate, Inc.

WOW! LOOK AT ALL THIS GOOD FOOD AND NEAT CLOTHING!
2-26

THIS IS GREAT STUFF

STAY OUT OF THE TRASH, GARFIELD
HOW DID YOU KNOW?
JIM DAVIS

WHAT A GLORIOUS MORNING!
2-27

I COULD REALLY ENJOY A MORNING LIKE THIS
JIM DAVIS
© 1984 United Feature Syndicate, Inc.

IF I COULD ONLY GET THIS CATCH OUT OF MY BACK

I GOTTA GET HELP FOR THIS CATCH IN MY BACK
JIM DAVIS
2-28

HEY, GUYS

WHAT WE HAVE HERE IS A FAILURE TO COMMUNICATE

MAYBE A GOOD NIGHT'S SLEEP WILL HELP ME GET RID OF THIS CATCH IN MY BACK
JIM DAVIS
2-29

MAYBE NOT

I HATE HAVING A CATCH IN MY BACK. I GET NO SLEEP, I GET NO FOOD, I GET NO EXERCISE

JIM DAVIS
3-1

DON'T TIP THE CAT OVER, ODIE
I GET NO RESPECT

WELL HELLO THERE, MR. STUCK-UP
JIM DAVIS
3-2

HAVING A CATCH IN ONE'S BACK DOES TEND TO GIVE ONE AN AIR OF SOPHISTICATION...

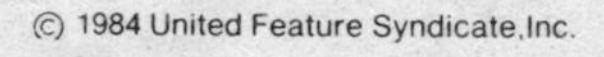

I COULD GET TO LIKE THIS

LET'S TAKE CARE OF THAT CATCH IN YOUR BACK, GARFIELD
JIM DAVIS

CRINK!

3-3

THERE YOU GO, OLD BUDDY
THANKS, I THINK

YOUR BIRTHDAY GIFT IS INSIDE THIS CARD, GARFIELD
JIM DAVIS 6-18

SOMEDAY, MY SIGNATURE WILL BE WORTH A LOT OF MONEY!

© 1983 United Feature Syndicate, Inc.

DON'T WORRY ABOUT YOUR CONDITION, GARFIELD
JIM DAVIS
8-12

YOU CAN STILL LEAD A USEFUL AND PRODUCTIVE LIFE

AS A PAPERWEIGHT, A DOORSTOP, A...
PUT YOUR FACE CLOSER TO THESE CLAWS
© 1983 United Feature Syndicate, Inc.

JIM DAVIS
6-5

SQUIRT

OKAY! WHO GREASED MY WIENER?!
© 1983 United Feature Syndicate, Inc.

GO FETCH THE PAPER, GARFIELD
12·28
JIM DAVIS

LOOK CLOSELY, JON. THESE ARE CAT'S PAWS, NOT SLAVE'S PAWS

I'LL IGNORE YOUR SMALL INDISCRETION THIS TIME, AND SPARE YOUR LIFE
THANK YOU, ... SIR

JIM DAVIS
8-29

THAT WASN'T VERY NICE, GARFIELD
IN THIS BUSINESS, "NICE" DOESN'T PUT BREAD ON THE TABLE
© 1983 United Feature Syndicate, Inc.

JIM DAVIS
1-17

I LOVE IT WHEN THEY ENTERTAIN ME

I'D BETTER SAVE SOME OF THIS BLUEBERRY PIE FOR JON. TO EAT IT ALL WOULD BE INCONSIDERATE AND SELFISH
JIM DAVIS
2-24

I AM WHAT I AM
© 1983 United Feature Syndicate, Inc.

DINNERTIME, GARFIELD!
JIM DAVIS
3-26
GARFIELD

BANZAI
GARFIELD

LD

I CAN'T BELIEVE I TURN SIX YEARS OLD TOMORROW. SOME CATS SAY, "LIFE BEGINS AT SIX," BUT I DON'T BUY THAT
JIM DAVIS
6-18

OLD AGE MAY TAKE ITS TOLL ON SOME CATS, BUT IT'S NOT GOING TO HAPPEN TO ME! I'M GOING TO DO SOMETHING ABOUT IT!

RIGHT AFTER MY NAP

HAPPY BIRTHDAY, GARFIELD! I GOT YOU A RUBBER CHICKEN. THEY'RE LOTS OF FUN!
WE'LL SEE ABOUT THAT
6-19
JIM DAVIS

SMACK
ODIE
SPLUT

CHICKEN, YOU AND I ARE GOING TO HAVE SOME GOOD TIMES

YOU NEED A NAME, FELLA. LET'S SEE... WHAT DO YOU NAME A RUBBER CHICKEN?
6·20
JIM DAVIS

RRRRR

"STRETCH"!
SNAP
© 1984 United Feature Syndicate,Inc.

PECK
PECK
PECK
JPM DAV!S
6-21

SMACK!

I'LL HAVE SOME HAM AND EGGS, AND MY FRIEND, STRETCH, WILL HAVE A BOWL OF RUBBER BANDS

PECK
PECK
PECK
JIM DAVIS
6-22

STOP PECKING ME WITH THAT RUBBER CHICKEN!

AW, LOOK, YOU HURT STRETCH'S FEELINGS
HE BRINGS OUT THE WORST IN ME

POOKY, I WOULD LIKE YOU TO MEET STRETCH, MY RUBBER CHICKEN
JIM DAVIS
6-23

QUITE FRANKLY, POOKY AND STRETCH DON'T HAVE A LOT OF PERSONALITY

BUT YOU HAVE TO TRADE OFF SOMETHING WHEN YOU SURROUND YOURSELF WITH GOOD LISTENERS

THEY SAY THE FIRST THING TO GO ON A CAT IS ITS HEARING
JIM DAVIS
6-17

OR WAS THAT EYESIGHT?

GARFIELD, IF YOU MESS WITH MY NEW FISH, YOU'LL REGRET IT
7-20
JIM DAVIS

WHAT'S SO REGRETTABLE ABOUT A LITTLE SEAFOOD SNACK?

JON'S GOING TO PAY FOR THIS

JIM DAVIS 7-21

WELL, WELL, ODIE. I SEE YOU DERIVE GREAT PLEASURE FROM OTHERS' MISFORTUNE

SO DO I !
SNAP!

OKAY, YOU TURKEYS, I'M PREPARED FOR ANYTHING
JIM DAVIS
7-19

♪AROOOO♫

CRASH!

WHY IS IT I GET BLAMED FOR EVERYTHING AROUND HERE? IF SOMETHING GOES WRONG, YOU JUST LAY IT ON OL' GARFIELD!

12-11

JIM DAVIS

OTHER GARFIELD BOOKS IN THIS SERIES

No. 1	Garfield The Great Lover	£1.95
No. 2	Garfield Why Do You Hate Mondays?	£2.50
No. 3	Garfield Does Pooky Need You?	£2.50
No. 4	Garfield Admit It, Odie's OK!	£2.50
No. 5	Garfield Two's Company	£1.95
No. 6	Garfield What's Cooking?	£2.50
No. 7	Garfield Who's Talking?	£1.95
No. 9	Garfield Here's Looking At You	£2.50
No. 10	Garfield We Love You Too	£1.95
No. 11	Garfield Here We Go Again	£1.95
No. 12	Garfield Life and Lasagne	£2.50
No. 13	Garfield In The Pink	£2.50
No. 14	Garfield Just Good Friends	£1.95
No. 15	Garfield Plays It Again	£2.50
No. 16	Garfield Flying High	£2.50
No. 17	Garfield On Top Of The World	£2.50
No. 18	Garfield Happy Landings	£2.50
No. 19	Garfield Going Places	£2.50
No. 20	Garfield Le Magnifique!	£2.50

LANDSCAPE SERIES

Garfield The All-Round Sports Star	£2.95
Garfield The Irresistible	£2.95
Garfield On Vacation	£2.95
Garfield Weighs In!	£2.95
Garfield I Hate Monday	£2.95
Garfield Special Delivery	£2.95
Garfield The Incurable Romantic	£2.95
Garfield Another Serve	£2.95
Garfield Wraps It Up	£2.95
Garfield This Is Your Life	£2.95
Garfield Sheer Genius	£2.95
Garfield Goes Wild	£2.95
Garfield Rebel Without A Clue!	£2.95

COLOUR TV SPECIALS

Here Comes Garfield	£2.95
Garfield On The Town	£2.95
Garfield In The Rough	£2.95
Garfield In Disguise	£2.95
Garfield In Paradise	£2.95
Garfield Goes To Hollywood	£2.95
A Garfield Christmas	£2.95
Garfield's Thanksgiving	£2.95

COLOUR TREASURIES

The Second Garfield Treasury	£5.95
The Third Garfield Treasury	£5.95
The Fourth Garfield Treasury	£5.95

Garfield A Weekend Away	£4.95
Garfield Book Of Cat Names	£2.50
Garfield Best Ever	£4.95
Garfield The Easter Bunny?	£3.95
Garfield How To Party	£3.95
Garfield Selection	£5.95
Garfield His 9 Lives	£5.95

All these books are available at your local bookshop or newsagent, or can be ordered direct from the publisher. Just tick the titles you require and fill in the form below. Prices and availability subject to change without notice.

Ravette Books Limited, 3 Glenside Estate, Star Road, Partridge Green, Horsham, West Sussex RH13 8RA

Please send a cheque or postal order and allow the following for postage and packing. UK: Pocket-books – 45p for one book, 20p for a second book and 15p for each additional book. Landscape Series – 50p for one book plus 30p for each additional book. TV Specials and Cat Names – 45p for one book plus 30p for each additional book. Other titles – 85p for one book plus 50p for each additional book ordered.

Name ....

Address ....

....